CW00859678

LEARNING WITH LLAMA

Book 1

To my Norwegian husband, Mark, thank you for taking me to your
homeland of Norway. It was there in the town of Skjolden that I met
The Llama, and was inspired by the breathtaking beauty of the land and the people.

To my children, Cody, Erik, and Kirin. Your fierce independence and support
of my dreams makes all things possible.

To COVID-19. Without you, I would not have had the time off work
that I needed to finish my book.

Hi! I am the Llama. Sometimes I'm in and sometimes I'm out.
Today, I am...out.

My name is Llama and I live in Norway,
today is bright and sunny, and so I can play.

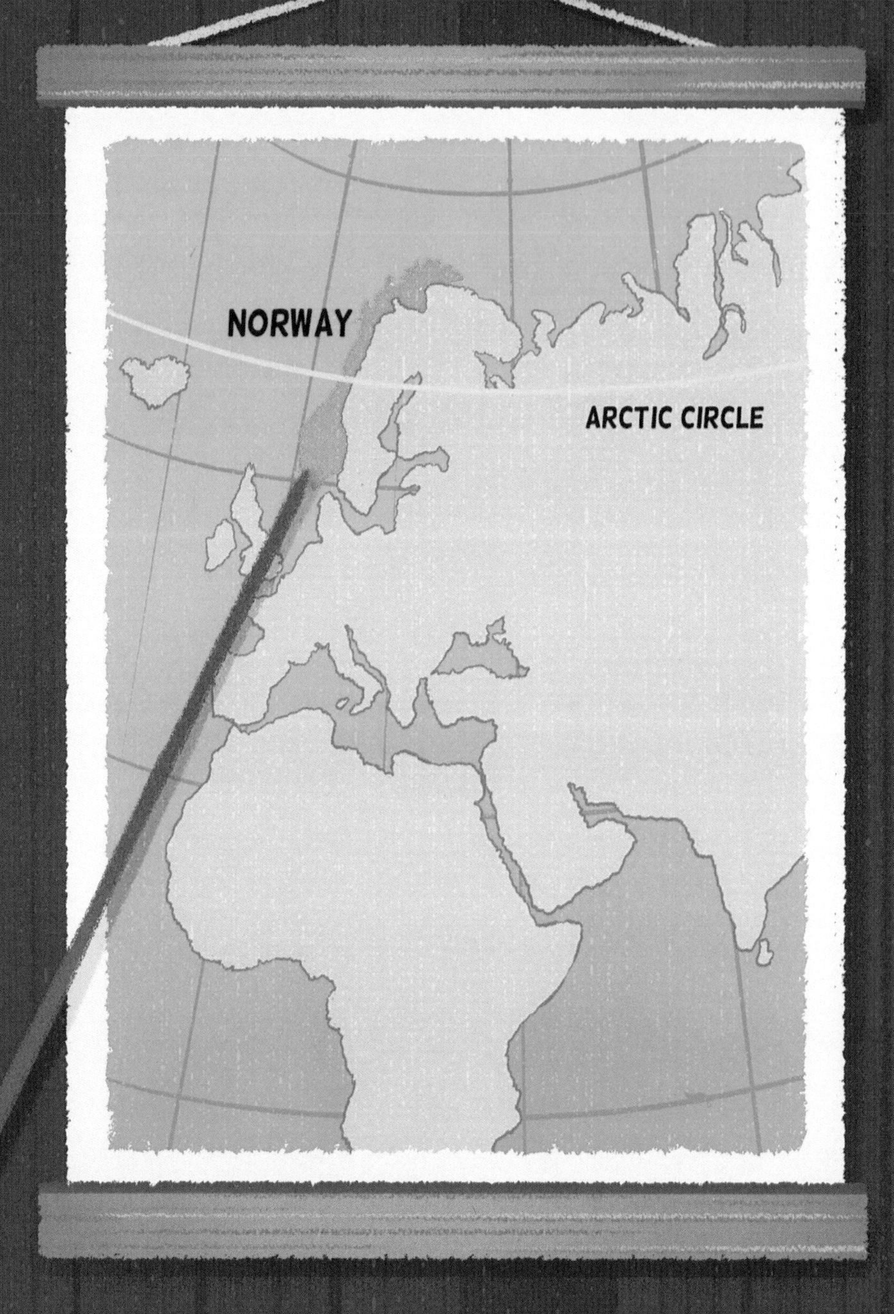

Norway is found near the top of the world,
below the Arctic Circle, where it's always so cold.

In the winter it's cold and there's lots of snow,
but when the summertime comes
the green starts to show.

The air is so clean and the flowers smell good.
Sometimes they're for sniffing and
sometimes they're for food.

Our brilliant blue waters in Norway are fjords,
boats, large and small, travel on them in hoards.

We see giant cruise ships and small boats for fishing.
There are kayaks, and crab catchers, and big nets for shrimping.

We also have boats that carry people and cars,
they're big and called ferries and can travel quite far.

The highways have to wind their way around all the water that is here, and surrounds the town.

From my home high up on the top of the hill,
I can see the boats, the town,
and the neighboring fields.

My friend Cow lives in the next pasture.
We race up and down the fence, but I think
I'm much faster.

We run and we play--my friend Cow is the best!
But Mama Llama will call and tell me to rest.

I follow her back to my bed for a nap,
I lay down my head and fall asleep in a snap.

There are many more animals that don't live on my farm,
like orcas in the ocean--they don't like it warm!

We also have reinder with big antlers on their heads,
just ilke the ones that pull Santa's sled.

Some sheds on my farm have roofs made of grass,
this keeps it cool in the summer 'til the heat starts to pass.

Goats climb to the top of the sheds,
and eat at the grass 'til they're fully fed.

My neighbor next door has a pretty red barn,
it houses the tools that he keeps on his farm.

There are tedders and inverters that speed up the drying,
of the hay that is cut as part of their farming.

Balers scoop the hay from the ground and wrap twine about.
Then the backdoor springs open and a big hay roll pops out!

There are lots and lots of these hay rolls in the field.
It's amazing how much one farm can yield.

It's getting colder now as the sun starts its slide,
'cross the sky, through the clouds, then behind the mountains to hide.

In the summer sometimes the sun never sets, it touches down,
almost gone, but doesn't disappear quite yet.

In Norway this is called the Midnight Sun,
it stays light all day and we play 'til we're done!

The lights start to twinkle in the village down below,
like the stars in the sky that are starting to show.

Mama Llama walks me in to put me to bed,
she scoots fresh hay all around my fuzzy head.

"But I am not sleepy," I say with a yawn,
but my eyes slowly close;
they won't open 'til dawn.

Mama Llama snuggles in and whispers so slight...
"Sleep well, my little Llama, I love you, good night."

The End!

Lightning Source UK Ltd.
Milton Keynes UK
UKRC010928091220
374765UK00001B/15